W9-CZY-152

THE OLD WOMAN AND HER MYSTERIOUS STORYBOOK, AND THE LITTLE GIRL WHO DIDN'T LIKE TO READ

An African Tale

K. CHRISTOPHER TOUSSAINT

Illustrated by HIGGINS BOND

United African Educational Foundation
Philadelphia, Pennsylvania

Published by the United African Educational Foundation

Phone: (215) 471-5119 Fax: (215) 726-1909

P.O. Box 42802, Philadelphia, PA 19101

E-mail: uaef@uaef.org; Website: www.uaef.org

This book is printed on acid-free paper that meets the American National Standard for Performance of Paper for Printed Library Materials.

Library of Congress Cataloging-in-Publication Data

K. Christopher Toussaint

THE OLD WOMAN AND HER MYSTERIOUS
STORYBOOK, AND THE LITTLE GIRL
WHO DIDN'T LIKE TO READ
An African Tale
Volume 3
ISBN 1-893811-03-4

This book is the third in a series of African fables and tales to be developed and issued by the United African Educational Foundation.

Printed in China

To my loving wife, Alice, without whose contributions
on the history of the ancient Benin Empire and otherwise
untiring support, this important book for young
people would not have been possible

United African Educational Foundation
Philadelphia, Pennsylvania

lifting the minds and aspirations
of our young that they may
lift our world to
a perfect
humanity

A Note From the Publisher

Teaching young people social values through the literature of fables and folktales can be immensely rewarding, and even pedagogically challenging. This African tale meets both these desired results in that it provides parents and teachers with a unique opportunity to share an important cross-cultural reading experience with their children or students.

One positive effect of television and movies in today's postmodern society is the fact that children are being exposed through these cultural icons to a more advanced vocabulary than they are usually taught in school. This means that they are being primed through these media to learn words beyond restrictive grade-level vocabularies. We have taken this phenomenon into full account by telling this story with a larger vocabulary than is usual for children's books. To address this innovation, we have provided an educational supplement at the end of the story that features a glossary of terms (including a comprehensive pronunciation key) that easily enables a child to look up and learn the meaning of a word that he or she has not yet been formally taught. The educational supplement also contains a list of thought-provoking questions about the story for discussion and essay writing. Perhaps the most innovative feature here for a children's book are a few word problems (featured in the supplement) that are based on various geometrical features of the story's physical setting. The supplement also provides a four–page narrative history of the ancient Benin Empire of sub-Saharan Africa, and a corresponding map delineating its physical contours and other prominent features. The supplement also contains a brief history and geography of the African continent (along with a corresponding map) and a linguistics section that features a brief introduction to the language of the people whose rich history and culture provided the impetus for this and other books in this series. Children and young students are bound to find these features challenging and rewarding with respect to their cognitive, analytical, reading, logicomathematical, and language-learning skills and abilities.

Although this tale contains a challenging vocabulary for most children, there are many children at the elementary-grade level who can read this book easily without the help of a parent or a teacher. But even these gifted and talented children will jump at a chance to share their impressions of this story and the other rich features in the book with an adult authority figure. Such a positive interaction between parent and child or teacher and student can only produce meaningful teaching-and-learning conversations and lively, animated discussions that can aid in both the intellectual and social development of the child and the broadening of his or her cultural outlook on the world.

There is a rich tradition in almost every African country of fables and tales used in the education of young children. These stories highlight moral and ethical aspects of human relationships and behavior in an easily understandable form. Walking through the streets of any one of these African cities or villages, on any given day, one is likely to see a throng of enthusiastic children gathered around a wise old sage to hear stories that have been handed down from generation to generation in the oral tradition of their ancient ancestral cultures. From *Aesop's* famous animal fables to *Anansi the Spider*, the consummate trickster in the Akan folktales, African fables and tales have been a valuable source of inspiration to virtually every culture in modern world history. *The Old Woman and Her Mysterious Storybook, and the Little Girl Who Didn't Like to Read* is written in the spirit of this great African tradition. This story's rich and exciting theme originated with the Edo-speaking people of what is present-day Nigeria, but it is a theme that is culturally universal in its moral and ethical meaning.

Edo is one of the multitudinous indigenous languages of West Africa and is spoken among the Bini ethnic. The Bini are a proud and creative people who inhabit a very old city in Nigeria's Midwestern region, called "Benin." Benin City is the governmental center of a legendary African empire whose monarchial social system is believed to predate that of the British monarchy, and its Edo-speaking people is believed to have settled in this tropical region for more than two millennia B.C.E. Commonly referred to as the "Ancient Kingdom of Benin" by world historians, this ancient African culture is renowned for having produced one of the world's most glorious artistic legacies in its awe-inspiring bronze castings and its elegant wood and ivory carvings and sculptures.

Nigeria is a young, budding democracy that boasts a population of more than 120 million people who together make up 250 different ethnolinguistic groups, the largest and most widely known of these being the Yoruba, the Hausa, and the Ibo. Nigeria is made up of 36 states with its federal capital (Abuja) situated near or at the country's geographical center. Nigeria has more than a hundred major universities and colleges. Of these, the University of Ibadan, the University of Ife, the University of Lagos, the University of Benin, the University of Nigeria, the University of Calabar, and Amadu Bello University are among the most universally known. The country covers an expanse of 356,669 square miles of lush green forests, life-sustaining rivers and waterways, agricultural plateaus, and rich mineral deposits.

The story of a little girl who is staunchly resistant to reading books, but whose obstinacy begins to fall apart when one day she encounters a persistent and caring old woman, is a vivid reflection of this fascinating geography and these rich cultures. As with all fables and tales, this one is both allegory and myth. But the constant and perennial struggle on the part of parents and schools to inspire young children to make reading books an integral and routine part of their daily lives is all too real and familiar. This allegorical tale, therefore, is likely to resonate morally with all who read it.

desuwa was an adorable little girl who lived in a village bordering a lively and bustling Nigerian city where she attended school and frequently visited to purchase food provisions for her mother. Adesuwa was exceedingly intelligent and an astute pupil in school, but she had a staunch aversion to reading books. She simply saw no sense in it, and thought reading books a total waste of valuable time.

No one could get Adesuwa to pick up a book and read, not even her parents or her teachers. Instead of reading, Adesuwa preferred spending her time playing soccer with her friends from whom she derived a great deal of enjoyment.

As Adesuwa was returning home to her village from school one day, playing merrily with her soccer ball along the way, as she usually did,

she inadvertently kicked her ball over a high fence into the compound of a reclusive old woman whom everybody in the village thought eccentric.

Without a second thought, Adesuwa crawled quickly through a small opening in the fence to retrieve her ball, feverishly searching through the thick overgrown weeds and undergrowth. "Come here little girl," the tired, trembling voice of the old woman called out to her.

Suddenly, Adesuwa realized what she had done, that she had entered onto the premises of the old woman about whom she had heard many strange rumors—the mysterious old woman who inspired a certain amount of foreboding in the hearts of even most of the grown ups in the village.

"Now come here little girl. I'm not going to hurt you," called the old woman, again.

hen suddenly, and before Adesuwa could move another muscle, the strange old woman was standing directly in front of her, close enough to reach out and grab her if she wanted to.

"Don't be afraid, little girl. I'm not going to hurt you," counseled the old woman. I have something to give you.

"You have something to give me?" asked Adesuwa, in a tone of caution and suspicion.

"Yes, it is a gift for you, and you've got to accept it," said the old woman, encouragingly.

desuwa instantly remembered the admonitions of her mother and father about accepting gifts from people whom she did not know.

"No, no, I cannot accept it unless you tell me what it is," Adesuwa protested. "Besides, my parents told me never to take gifts from strangers."

"Oh, but I'm hardly a stranger, little girl,"
the old woman vaunted. "I'm the old grandma
of this whole province, waving a hand wide
in the air as if to indicate all of the surrounding
villages and the entire city. "But you're too
young to know that, aren't you? Anyway,
what I have here is not an ordinary gift,"
advised the old woman. "It's a special gift,
and it really is just for you."

"Just for me!" replied Adesuwa, astonished.
"But you don't know me. How could the gift
be just for me when you don't even know me?"

he Old Woman sensed that Adesuwa was extremely strong-willed and sagacious well beyond her years, but she pressed on.

"Tell me little girl," asked the old woman, "do you like to read books?"

"Read books!" exclaimed Adesuwa, alarmingly. "Of course not! I absolutely abhor reading books."

"Then this gift is surely for you, said the old woman.

"No! I'm not going to take it," Adesuwa scoffed, placing emphasis on each of her words. "I do not like to read books!"

"But why on earth don't you like to read books, little girl?" inquired the old woman.

"Because it's simply no fun reading books," Adesuwa responded.

desuwa's iron-like tenacity was beginning to wear on the old woman, but she continued to press on.

"Aren't you even curious about what the gift is?" asked the old woman.

"Yes," replied Adesuwa. "I must admit,
I am curious to know what it is."

"It is a special book I have for you,"
said the old woman.

"A book!" exclaimed Adesuwa in a tone
of revulsion. "Now I know I won't take it,
because I most assuredly, most definitely,
and most positively will not read it!"

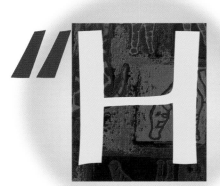"Here, Let me show you the book," the old woman persisted, as she removed a tattered, aged-looking book from an old burlap sack she held in her hand.

"Listen carefully, little girl," said the old woman, beguilingly. "This is by no means an ordinary book; this is a special book. Yes, it is a special and a mysterious book. If you open the book and read one page, you will experience more fun than you've ever had before, just by reading one, solitary page."

The Ancient Benin Empire

ut Adesuwa held her ground, standing arm-folded before the old woman, as if to dramatize her dogged sense of purpose and determination.

The old woman realized that Adesuwa wasn't going to give an inch and that she had to try a more subtle approach to get her to acquiesce in taking the book.

"'ll tell you what," counseled the old woman, tactfully. "Take the book home with you and think about it. Whenever you're feeling really bored and tired of playing the same old games, just open the book and read one page, and I solemnly promise—you will experience more fun than imaginable."

"All right, all right old grandma," said Adesuwa, with a sigh of resignation. "I'll take the book home and put it on my shelf as you have suggested, but I'm not going to read it—not even one sentence."

"It's a deal," said the old woman.

Beaming with elation, the old woman placed the old, tattered book gently into Adesuwa's hands.

 desuwa immediately ran home and placed the book on her bookshelf where there lay several other books that she had not read or opened.

She then hastily changed from her school uniform to one of her favorite dresses and went out immediately to play soccer with some of her friends.

hat night, as Adesuwa lay awake in her bed, thinking about all the fun she had had playing with her soccer ball and her friends that day, she heard a faint, tiny voice coming from the direction of her bookshelf.

"Read me! Read me!" said the voice. Adesuwa suddenly realized that the voice was coming from the book the old woman had given her.

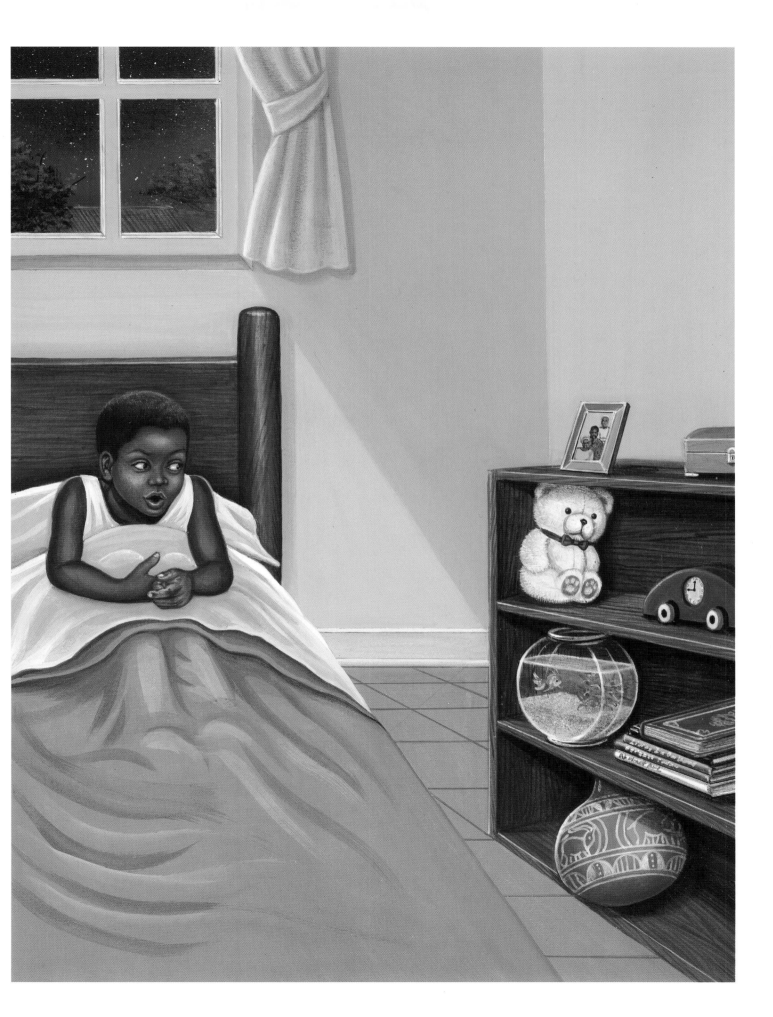

his revelation startled Adesuwa to her feet. She then became even more alarmed upon remembering what the old woman had told her about the mysterious nature of the storybook.

But Adesuwa's razor-sharp mind quickly suggested to her that what her eyes and ears were at that moment perceiving was not possible.

"Wait a minute! A book is an inanimate object, and I've learned in school that all inanimate objects are inorganic and lifeless things that cannot possibly talk. I must be dreaming," said Adesuwa with a note of incredulity.

"No, you're hardly dreaming," responded the mysterious storybook. "It is really I who am speaking."

"What do you want with me?" asked Adesuwa, disbelievingly. "I want you to read me," responded the storybook. "You will have more fun than you can possibly fathom if you do."

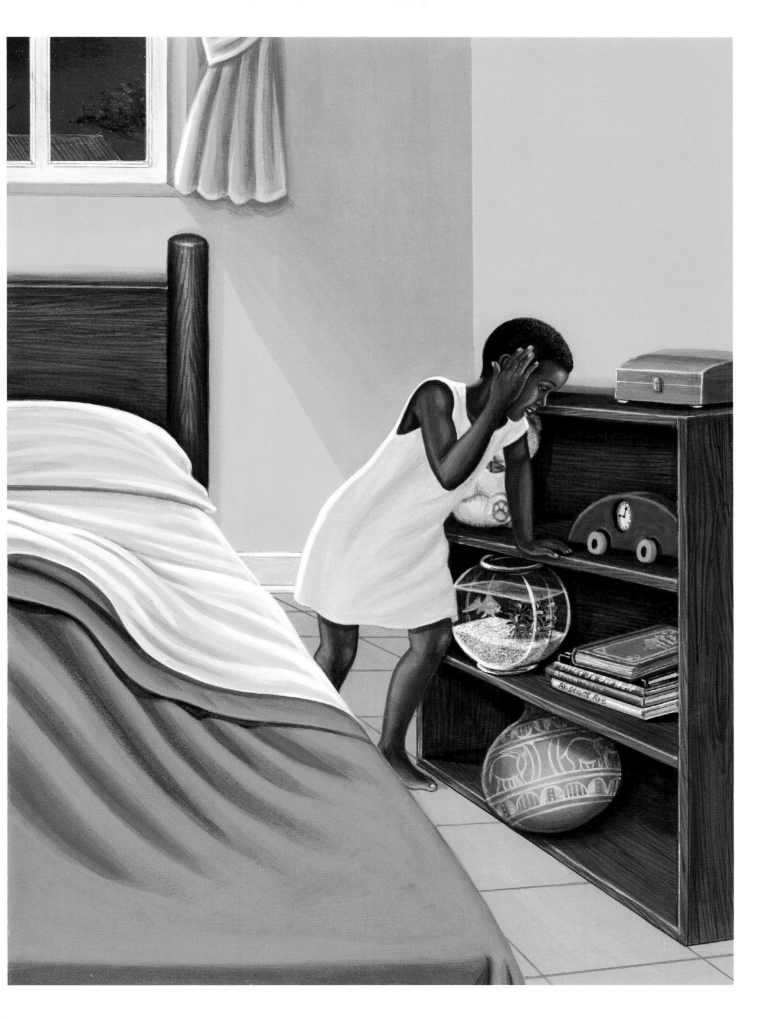

"There is no fun in reading books," Adesuwa replied.

"But, I'll bet if you read me, you will have lots of fun—more than ever before," said the mysterious storybook.

"No, I won't. I know I won't have any fun reading you, because all books are hopelessly boring," said Adesuwa.

"Are you quite sure about that?" asked the mysterious storybook. "Yes, I am completely sure," responded Adesuwa.

"Well, let's make a wager," said the mysterious storybook. "If you read one page of me, and if it does not provide you with great fun and enjoyment, I will not bother you ever again."

"Ok, it's a deal!" exclaimed Adesuwa, excitedly. "Remember," Adesuwa reminded the mysterious storybook, "I am to read one page only, and if it does not provide me with fun and enjoyment as you have promised, you will not bother me

The Ancient Benin Empire

...ing In Our World

...ca Today

Abstract Art by Simon Smith

again forever and forever. That is the deal, right?"

"Right," responded the mysterious storybook.
"That is the deal."

eeling completely triumphant, Adesuwa took the book down from the bookshelf, opened it and began to read aloud, just to assure the mysterious storybook that she was really and truly reading it.

"Once upon a time, in an ancient African kingdom called Benin," Adesuwa began, "there lived a generous king, called an Ogiso, who spent a great portion of his immense wealth to build a university for little children…"

As Adesuwa read, she felt a great gush of exhilaration that somehow catapulted her more than a thousand years back in time to the Ancient Kingdom of Benin.

The ancient city seemed a perfectly salubrious place. It was quiet and serene with immaculate streets and colorful buildings, and scores of fashionably dressed men and women happily going to and fro.

Adesuwa was mesmerized by the beauty of all she saw—a group of musicians, an iron and bronze sculptor busily fashioning art for the royal palace, an exquisitely sculptured water fountain that sat in front of the palace gate, and many other splendid things.

hen there was the royal Court of the Oba, filled with courtiers, servants, distinguished dignitaries and local villagers.

desuwa ran excitedly about the ancient city trying to see as much as she could. There were so many exciting things to see.

Adesuwa had head her parents and teachers talk about the Ancient Kingdom of Benin, but she never dreamt it was anything like what she was then experiencing firsthand.

She never knew that the ancient city she had heard the elders sing about was laid out with such architectural splendor and magnificence. She never knew about the long procession of great Ogisos, Obas and Queen Mothers in her Bini ancestry. The more she saw in the ancient city, the more she wanted to see. Everything to Adesuwa was all so exciting and all so wonderful.

eeling totally exhausted from having run all over the ancient city, Adesuwa flopped down on the steps of the great palace of the Ogiso to take a rest.

But, suddenly and mysteriously, she found herself back in her room again sitting in her bed reading the last two words on the last page in the mysterious storybook, which read: "The End." Without realizing or intending it, Adesuwa had read the entire book.

"Wow! What a book! She exclaimed. "What a magnificently delicious book!" she shouted again as she ran excitedly through the house to tell her parents of all she had read and learned.

As Adesuwa narrated her wonderful experience to her astonished parents, she glanced out the window and saw the mysterious old woman who had given her the book standing casually outside her window.

The old woman smiled knowingly at Adesuwa and went on her way. Adesuwa smiled knowingly back at the old woman as she continued her amazing narrative to her completely dumbfounded parents.

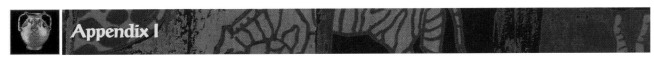

Pronunciation Key

Vowel Sounds

Symbols	Key Words				
a	bat, act, marry	e	ten, edge, set	i	is, mirror, big
ā	ape, play, pail	ē	even, bee, equal	ī	ice, bite, pie
ä	pot, father, part	ĕ	pet, fret, met	ĭ	pit, it, itch
ã	pat, axe, sat			î(r)	pier, steer, mere
â(r)	air, dare, scare	ə	alone, edible, system		
o	ox, box, rock	oi	noise, oil, joint	u	unity
ō	over, no, toe	o͞o	took, tune, too	ŭ	fun, run, bun
ŏ	pot, rot, tot	o͝o	boot, book, look	û(r)	urge, burn, term
ô	all, ball, for	ou	out, sour, cow		

Consonant Sounds

Symbols	Key Words				
b	back, bed, bib	l	let, lid, mellow	w	away, wet, witch
d	dog, do, deed	m	my, mum, meet	y	yes, onion, canyon
f	phone, fit, rough	n	no, now, net	z	zoo, those, rise
g	get, give, gag	p	put, pop, pot	ch	chew, punch, nature
h	hat, hear, hope	r	roar, red, read	sh	shoe, fashion, shell
hw	which, nowhere	s	sauce, sit, see	th	then, thin, either
j	just, joy, badge	t	tight, top, ten	zh	beige, mirage, garage
k	keep, kick, cat	v	value, voice, live		

NOTE: The stress symbol (ˈ) is used to indicate that the syllable with which the symbol is used is to be stressed or emphasized. A bold stress symbol (ˈ) means that the strongest emphasis or stress is placed on the syllable. A light stress symbol (ˈ) means that less stress is placed on the syllable, but slightly more than would be placed on the syllable that had no stress symbol.

Vocabulary Words and Definitions

KEY WORDS FROM THE STORY

abhor • ab-hor (ab-hôr′) tr.v. To regard with horror or loathing

acquiesce • ac-qui-esce (ăk′wē-ĕs′) intr.v. To consent or comply positively

admonitions • ad-mon-ni-tion (ăd′mənish′ən) n. A warning to correct some fault; a mild rebuke

assuredly • as-sured-ly (ə-shoord′ ĭd lē) adv. Certain; confidently

aversion • a-ver-sion (ə-vû′shən) n. A fixed, intense dislike

beguilingly • be-guil-ing-ly (bĭ-gīl′ĭng lē) adv. To amuse, charm, mislead, or deceive

courtier • cour-ti-er (kôr′ tē-ər) n. An attendant at a sovereign's (king's) court

dourly • dour-ly (door′ lē) adv. Ill-humoredly, gloomily

eccentric • ec-cen-tric (ĭk-sĕn′ trĭk) adj. Strange, odd, unconventional

elation • e-la-tion (ē lā′ shən) n. A feeling of exultant joy or pride

exceedingly • ex-ceed-ing-ly (ĭk-sē′dĭng-lē) adv. Extremely; to a great degree

exhilarate • ex-hil-a-rat-ed (ĭg zĭl′ərāt′ed) tr.v. To cause to feel happily refreshed and energetic; to stimulate

exquisitely • ex-qui-site-ly (ĕk′ skwĭ-zĭt-ly) adv. Intricately and beautifully design; elaborately made

feverishly • fe-ve-rish-ly (fē′vər-ĭsh-lə) adv. Greatly excited; marked by intense activity

foreboding • fore-bod-ing (fôr-bō′ dĭng) v. A sense of impending evil

inadvertently • in-ad-ver-tent-ly (ĭn′ əd-vûr′ tnt-lē) adj. Marked by unintentional lack of care; unintentional

inanimate • in-an-i-mate (ĭn-ăn′ə-mĭt) adj. Not having the qualities associated with active, living organisms

incredulity • in-cre-du-li-ty (ĭn′ krĭ-dōō′ lĭ-tē) n. The state or quality of being incredulous (disbelieving); inability to believe

inorganic • in-or-ga-nic (ĭn′ ôr-găn′ ĭk) adj. Not having the organized structure of living things; composed of matter that is not animal or vegetable

mesmerized • mes-me-rized (mĕz′mə-rīzed) tr.v. To spellbind; enthrall

reclusive • re-clu-sive (rĭ-klōō′sĭv) adj. Seeking or preferring seclusion or isolation; shut away from the world

resignation • res-ig-na-tion (rĕz′ ĭg-nā′ shən) n. Unresisting acceptance of something as inescapable; submission

sagacity • sa-ga-city (sə-gă′ĭ-tē) n. Penetrating intelligence and sound judgment; farsighted; keen perception

salubrious • sa-lu-bri-ous (sə-lōō′ brē-əs) adj. Conducive or favorable to health and well-being; wholesome

sigh • sigh (sī) v. To exhale audibly in a long, deep breath, as in weariness or relief

staunch • staun-ch (stäunch) adj. Firm and steadfast

tenacity • te-nac-i-ty (tə-năs′ ĭ-tē) n. The state or quality of being tenacious (tending to hold persistently to something, such as a point of view)

triumphant • tri-um-phant (trī-ŭm′ fənt) adj. Exulting in success or victory; rejoicing for victory

vaunt • vaunt (vônt) tr.v. To speak boastfully of; brag about

Appendix II

Try To Answer These Questions

1. Explain the moral of the story.
2. A tale is a myth or a story that is not "real," but is still true to life. Explain what bearing, if any, this tale might have on everyday life.
3. Explain in what ways have this story helped you, or can be useful to you as an individual person.
4. Can you think of an occasion where you became a greatly inspired or enlightened by a book you read.
5. Do you think Adesuwa will continue to read books? (Explain why or why not.)
6. What would you recommend that teachers do to get young students to read more?
7. How would you describe the relationship between the old woman and the little girl?
8. Explain why reading books should be considered a value.

Map of Benin City

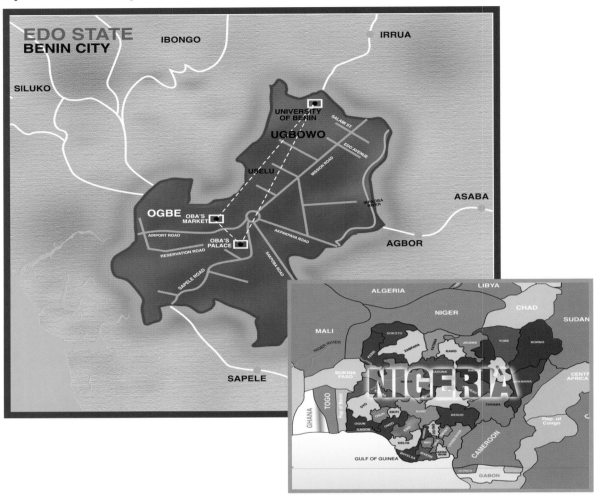

Try To Solve These Math Problems

1. Adesuwa's cousin, Osameyan, is a research fellow at the University of Benin who travels back-and-forth to the Oba's palace every day. Osameyan normally walks at a rate of 6.4 km per hour and takes 1.5 hrs to travel roundtrip between the two locations. What is the distance in kilometers from the Oba's palace to the university? What is the distance in miles?

2. Assuming that the distance between the University of Benin and the Oba's market is 4 km, what is the distance between the Oba's market and the Oba's palace?
   (Hint: Use the dotted right triangle between the three locations on the map, and also use the Pythagorean theorem).

3. Adesuwa takes 33 minutes at a rate of 4.5ft per sec to walk to the Oba's market. Adesuwa's house is situated along a straight line directly east of the Oba's market. What is the distance in miles between Adesuwa's house and the Oba's market? Approximately where on the map is Adesuwa's house located?
   (Hint: Assume that North is in the direction of the University of Benin).

4. Adesuwa makes regular visits to the Oba's Market to buy special cooking items for her mother. On a particular day, Adesuwa's mother gave her 1,560 naira (Nigerian currency) to buy a variety of food items from the Oba's market. The exchange rate in U.S. dollars at the time of purchase was 130 naira to 1 U.S. dollar. Adesuwa bought several food items for an equivalent of 9.5 U.S. dollars. How much money (if any) does Adesuwa have left (in naira) after her purchases?

A Brief Introduction to the Edo Language

Apart from the proposition that learning can be fun, learning another language opens up many possibilities for educational and cultural enlightenment. A child who learns to speak a few words or phrases in a different language will likely feel an added sense of self-confidence and self-worth. In addition, learning the language of a different culture can be an effective route to understanding the ways of its people, and it can bring into clearer focus the reality of the existence in the world of viable cultures other than one's own. Although the girl and the strange old woman are obviously fictional, the place from which (Edo State, Nigeria) and the people from whom (the Bini) this story is drawn are very real. The Binis are a people steeped in rich culture, ancestral tradition, and ancient history. Below are a few common greetings, sentences, and words and phrases from their language.

Common Greetings

Edo	Pronunciation	English
Ọbokhian	(Awh-bow-heae)	Welcome
Ọbowa	(Awh-bow-wa)	Greetings to you at home
Wábowa	(Wa-bow-wa)	Greetings to everyone at home
Koyọ	(Ko-yo)	Hello
Dómo	(Doe-mo)	Hello to an elderly person
V'bọye hé?	(Woe-yeh-heh)	How are you? How is it?
Ọyẹse	(Awh-yeh-see)	I am fine. It is fine.
Ọbowiẹ	(Awh-bow-hwer)	Good morning
Ọbavan	(Awh-ba-von)	Good afternoon
Ọbota	(Awh-bow-tar)	Good evening
Ọkhiowiẹ	(Awh-huen-hwer)	Goodnight

A Few Basic Sentences

Edo	Pronunciation	English
Vb'a tie rhue'?	(Var-tea-ru-e'?)	What is your name?
Adesuwa e' a' tie mwen, men Ihoni gha ti e'be.	(Awesuwa Ai-ar-tea-wen, mey-ẽ-hoe-knee-yaw-tea-e' bay)	I'm called Adesuwa, and I like to read.
Vbua rie?	(Woe- re eh')	Where are you going?
Ti rọ waebe.	(Tea-re-o-way-bay)	I am going to school.
Ini igho nôn?	(E-knee-go-non?)	How much is it?
Ẹ naira eva nôn.	(Eh-naira-ehva non.)	It is two naira.
Vbo ye he?	(Woe-yeh-heh?)	How are you?
Ọ yê sẽ.	(Awh-yeh-see.)	I am fine.
Adesuwa	(Ar-dey-sue-wa)	Coming into wealth

Pronunciation Key

Pronounce *a* as the *a* in car; *e* as the *e* in Edward; *ẹ* as the e in pet; *i* as the *i* in ski; *o* as the *o* in old; *ọ* as awh; *u* as the *u* in universe.

African History-World History

Edo Artist, (Benin) Nigeria
Bronze Plaque with King and Entourage
Middle period: circa 17th century, 20 in
National Museum, Lagos, Nigeria

Learning about ancient cultures and world histories can be both educationally enriching and personally satisfying. A child with a firm grounding in world history is likely to experience a heightened cognition and intellect and develop a broadened cultural outlook on the world. Although the story of *The Old Woman and Her Mysterious Storybook, and the Little Girl Who Didn't Like to Read* is allegorical, the geographical setting of the story and its people and culture are very real. The illustrated bronze castings and ivory and wood carvings featured variously in the book are also true and accurate representations of some of the exquisite works of royal art (now world-renowned) produced by the ancient Benin Empire, or the Edo-speaking people of Nigeria. What follows is a brief chronicle of this incredible empire.

The Benin Empire

Of the many great empires that dotted the pre-colonial West African landscape, including that of the Ashanti and the Oyo, the Benin Empire was by far the most stable and enduring. This ancient empire lies in the tropical rain forest of West Africa in what is present-day Nigeria. Nigeria is bounded on the north by the Republic of Niger, on the east by Chad and Cameroon, on the south by the Gulf of Guinea, and on the west by the Republic of Benin (formally known as Dahomey, and no relation to the ancient Benin Empire or the Edo-speaking people of Nigeria). History shows that ancestral Binis occupied this tropical region for well over two thousand years B.C.E. Their sedentary presence in the region was the result of waves of culturally similar African populations migrating from east and northeast Africa (mainly from Egypt and the Sudan) and assimilating into the indigenous population. This prolific form of cultural miscegenation in the specific region lasted for scores upon scores of generations, producing stable and thriving social organizations that ultimately evolved into a cohesive culture and a unified and productive society. Benin as an empire proper, however, had its beginnings in 800 B.P. (before the present), which marked the appearance of the first dynasty. The empire flourished in art and commerce through the nineteenth century until, in 1897, the British destroyed it in what world historians call "the British punitive expedition in Benin City." Although the assault was widely heralded by the British as a justified response for the Binis' having previously killed several officers of the British Crown sent to see the Oba on a peace mission, their primary aim, history shows, was to punish the existing king (Oba Ovonramwen) for his refusal to grant the British their request for untrammeled and unregulated trade with the Bini people and free, strategic access through Benin territory to bordering local governments and townships for the same exploitative purpose. Although the British razed the royal palace of the Oba and looted and carted away literally tons of priceless treasures in the form of exquisite works of royal art (the illustrated representations of ancient Benin art shown in this book are like a single drop of water among a whole ocean of these great treasures), this ancient civilization was ultimately able to rebound, though it had lost control over the vast territories once under its orbit. Today, in spite of the fact that Nigeria is a nation–state with a president and a national legislative assembly, all but a few of the monarchial customs and practices of the royal court of the ancient Obas of Benin survive intact under the reign of the present king, Oba N'Edo Uku Akpolokpolo Eradiauwa.

How It Began

As noted above, 800 B.P. represents the appearance of the first Benin dynasty. This was the dynasty of the *Ogiso*, translated in the Bini language (Edo) as "the Ruler of the Sky" (*Ogie* as ruler or king, *iso* as sky). The substantial history on the Benin Empire shows that the establishment of the dynasty and kingdom grew out of an organized council of elders who had the popular support of the provincial chiefs who, in turn, enjoyed the popular support of the villagers and the general Bini masses. The first dynasty consisted of thirty-one rulers, with the first Ogiso, Igodo, giving Benin its name, Igodomigodo, which means "City of Cities" or "Land of Igodo" in the Bini language. When Igodo (the first dynastic king) died after a long reign, he was succeeded on the throne by his eldest son, Ere, who was said to be a man of peace and vision and was popularly known for his prudent and sagacious management of the affairs of the realm. Ere introduced important reforms and improvements in the empire. One such reform or improvement was his establishment of an association of royal chroniclers (*Ughoron*) who were required to preserve through recitation the birth and death dates of each of the rulers and the most important events occurring during their individual reigns. Ere is also credited with laying the foundation of what is known as "King Makers" (*Uzama Nihinron*)of the first dynasty. He is even said to be responsible for the establishment of artisan guilds, such as those of bronze of brass casters, ivory and wood carvers, leather workers, weavers, carpenters, and the like. The lives of these highly skilled individuals were devoted exclusively to the production of exquisite art for the royal palace for which they were handsomely rewarded and honored by the king. These individuals (mostly men) enjoyed the protection of the Ogiso and were respected by the rest of the royal court attendants and courtiers. Ere (again, the first Ogiso of the second dynasty) is also believed to have introduced the various emblems of Benin royalty, which prevails to the present. The most notable of these emblems include the rectangular royal throne (*agba*), the round leather fan, the round containers of bark and hide, and the ceremonial sword (*ada*). Of all the various royal emblems, the sword was one of the most symbolically powerful and was one of the objects placed prominently on an ancestral altar. The presence of the sword on the altar symbolized the ancestors' power and authority over the course of events in the kingdom. Other royal insignia that Ere is credited with introducing are ankle and neck rings made of pears and forged or embossed brass. Although the first dynasty consisted of thirty-one Ogisos, with the exception of Ere and the last Ogiso, Owodo, little is known about the specific affairs of the other rulers of this dynastic period. However, at least half of the names of these Ogisos have been preserved by way of the royal chroniclers.

According to the Bini chroniclers, the kings of Benin sent their sons (the royal princes) to preside over the surrounding provinces and villages so as to preserve the necessary renewal of the latter's submission to each succeeding Ogiso through tributes and oaths of allegiance. Each prince was given a royal title (and a sinecure) that reflected his nobility and signified his status in relation to his brothers (each of the Ogisos had many sons) as a potential hereditary legatee to the throne. The Ogiso dynasty lasted for nearly four centuries—ending somewhere between 1150 and 1200 B.P.

Around 1200 B.P., the new dynasty (the second period) of the *Obas* emerged. The first ruler of the new dynasty, Oranmiyan, a Yoruba, was not very successful in ruling the Binis, mainly because he was of a different ethnicity and did not speak the Edo language very well nor understand Bini customs or culture. Thus his son, *Eweka I*, succeeded him and became king under the title "Oba," a title that all succeeding kings of Benin have bore.

Edo Artist, (Benin) Nigeria
Pair of leopards – Middle period, Mid-16th century, Bronze, 19.8 in and 19 in National Museum, Lagos, Nigeria

The Social Structure of the Royal Kingdom

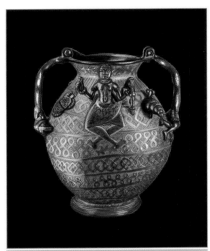

Edo Artist, (Benin) Nigeria
Ceremonial-Ritual container – Bronze, 9 in
Middle period: 17th century
National Museum, Lagos, Nigeria

The ancient kingdom of Benin was a hierarchically structured society, socially stratified by hereditary title and nobility status. As in any monarchy, the Oba, or king, stood at the top of the hierarchy and wielded absolute power. Standing directly below the Oba in the hereditary line of descent and title was his first son who was given the title "Edaiken" upon reaching the age of majority. Before reaching this age, the eldest son bore the title "Oko," which distinguished him from his brother princes who bore the title "Okoro." Each of the princes was given charge over a large province, or principality, within the kingdom. The daughters of the Oba bore the title "Uvbi" (Princess). Benin was both a patriarchal and a patrilineal society. Hence, it was not common for the princesses to rule over villages and provinces as did the kings' sons. Being of royal birth, however, the princesses did enjoy the honor, prestige, wealth, and social status of the highest nobility in the realm. Next in rank were powerful chiefs who were appointed by the Oba. All of the chiefs were part of the nobility class and were both feared and respected by the masses. After the chiefs ranked the royal artisans who, as already noted, also held high status in the kingdom. These individuals, however, did not hold any political office or title. The general masses of the Bini people rested at the bottom of the hierarchy, but individuals from among the masses frequently rose to higher status or lofty position in the kingdom, and even to the rank of chieftaincy.

Benin Royal Art

During what is known as its classical age (from the fourteenth through the fifteenth century), Benin produced one of the world's most glorious artistic legacies in its awe-inspiring bronze castings and elegant wood and ivory carvings and sculptures. These magnificent works of art were created by the skilled artisans, under the direct commission of the Obas, to reflect the grandeur of the royal court. These works of art included, among other things, human and animal figures, some in the form of commemorative heads of Obas and Queen Mothers, and relief plaques depicting the Oba and members of the royal court. Also included among these works were pendants, bracelets, elephant tusks, and ivory carvings of birds, animals, and objects that symbolized the power and splendor of the royal court. The producers of these works of art were organized into guilds and held a higher status than their counterparts who produced works of art for foreign visitors and the general Bini population. Among the producers of palace art, the bronze or brass casters held a particularly high social status. These artisans were directly under the Oba's control, as noted earlier, and their workshops were situated inside the palace grounds, unlike artisans of other specialties who were located in workshops in proximity to, but outside the palace walls.

Present-Day Benin

Today, the Benin monarchy continues, though its power is restricted mainly to Benin City and surrounding villages. The royal palace of the Oba is still located in Benin City, where it was during the reign of the Obas of old. The Bini chiefs are still under the authority of the Oba. The Bini people are progressive and productive in education and commerce and, like their counterparts in Britain, they are romantically wedded to the idea of monarchy. Indeed, they thoroughly adore the Oba and all of the trappings of kingship. Within the kingdom, land is still allocated by the Oba or one of his appointed nobles. In present-day Nigeria, the Oba of Benin does not participate in politics, as did his predecessors of old. But it is not uncommon today for state governors, and sometimes heads of state or presidents, to seek audience with this highly respected monarch for council and advice. Benin history continues to be an integral part of the substantive education of primary and secondary schoolchildren throughout Benin City and all other parts of Nigeria.

Brief Facts About the Ashanti and Oyo Empires

The land of the ancient Ashanti Empire lies in what is present-day Ghana (between latitude 4° 45' N. and latitude 10° 10' N.), which is situated on the south coast of West Africa and positioned slightly below present-day Nigeria and above the equator. Ghana is made up of numerous ethnic groups, with the Ashanti being the most numerous and politically powerful.

The ancient Oyo Empire was situated above the equator, west of the Benin Empire. It had the same parallel with that of both the Benin and the Ashanti Empires (between about 4° 30' and latitude 14° 17' N.). The Oyo Empire was made up of a powerful and progressive people, called the "Yoruba." History shows that the Benin Empire once ruled over the Oyo Empire, which evidently explains why the kings of the latter empire also bore the title "Oba" (a distinctively Benin name and title).

The Last Oba of the Ancient Benin Empire and the Present Oba of the New Benin Kingdom

Oba Ovonramwen was the last Oba of the truly ancient Benin Empire (the British forced him into exile in 1897). His successors, especially the present Oba (Eradiauwa), presided over the new Benin Kingdom that still retains all but a few of the royal trappings of its ancient predecessors.

Edo Artist, (Benin) Nigeria
Head of Queen Mother – Early period.
Early 16th century, Bronze, 20 in
National Museum, Lagos, Nigeria

Important Names, Concepts, and Titles

Edo (E-do) – the language of the Benin people. This language is extremely complicated for outsiders, and it is as old as the Bini people themselves. **Ogiso** (O-gi-so) – the title of the kings of the first Benin dynasty. **Dynasty** – an organized social system characterized by a succession of rulers who are members of the same family. **Ughoron** (Ug-gho-ron) – the Bini name for an association of royal chroniclers or reporters who were charged with keeping a record of the affairs of the various kings through oral recitation, as well as their birth and death records.

Uzama Nihinron (U-za-ma Ni-hin-ron) – the royal name of the "King Makers," the group of elderly men who "handled" the heir apparent and delivered him to the throne by managing and coordinating all of the ceremonies and rituals he had to perform before being crowned. **Igodomigodo** I-go-do-migo-do) – The original name of Benin City in the Edo language. In translation, it is "City of Cities" or "Land of Igodo." **Igodo** (I-go-do) – the name of the first king, or Ogiso of the first Benin dynasty. **Ere** – the name of the second king, or Ogiso of the first Benin dynasty. **Ada** – the Bini name for the royal ceremonial sword that symbolized the power of the king. **Agba** – the name of the royal throne of the kings or Ogisos of the ancient Benin Empire. **Owodo** (O-wo-do) – the name of the last Ogiso of the first Benin dynasty. **Artisan Guild** – an association of individuals of a trade (e.g., bronze casters) whose organized membership provides protection for each individual

Edo Artist, (Benin) Nigeria
Head of a Leopard - 17th Century
Ivory, brass tack, and iron nails, 6 1/4 in
Collection: A. Maschmann.

member, and whose members are charged with maintaining high standards in the particular craft. The Benin Empire boasted many such artisan guilds.

Africa is the second largest continent of the seven great divisions of land that make up the earth's surface. It is immense in its proportions—comprising roughly 12 million square miles of arable land, rain forests, deserts, and vital waterways. Africa is separated from Asia by the Red Sea and the Suez Canal and from Europe by the Mediterranean Sea. It is bounded by the Indian Ocean on its eastern part and the Atlantic Ocean on its western part. Africa is shown to be the ancestral birthplace of all of humankind, a fact scientifically upheld over the last three-quarters of a century by a wealth of anthropological, archaeological, and paleontological discoveries. Two of the most dramatic of these discoveries are the 3-million-year-old fossilized remnants of a female *Australopithecus afarensis* (Lucy) that was unearthed in a remote gorge in the Afars region of Ethiopia in 1972 by French anthropologist Maurice Taieb and his team, and the skull of a 2-milion-year- old hominid discovered in a gully near Lake Turkana in Kenya in the same year by British anthropologist Richard Leakey, son of famed anthropologists Louis and Mary Leakey. Just as dramatic is the discovery of 5.7 million-year-old fossils in Ethiopia believed to be the remains of humankind's earliest known ancestor. These primordial remains (called *Ardipithecus*) were dug up in the Awash desert region of Ethiopia in 2001 by Yohannes Halie-Selassie, an Ethiopian anthropologist from the University of California at Berkley. Apart from all these great discoveries, the cutting-edge science of population genetics has made it possible today to create a family tree for the whole of humanity. Using DNA mapping, Oxford University geneticist Spencer Wells has been able to demonstrate conclusively that every living person today is a descendent from one man who lived in Africa 60,000 years ago. Today, some 900 million people inhabit the African continent; more than 95 percent of whom are dark skinned, or are what anthropologists have called "Negroid." Taken together, these peoples constitute more than two thousand

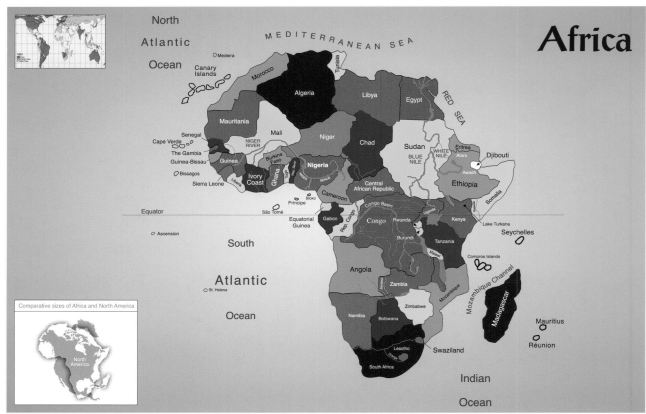

different ethnic groups and speak as many indigenous languages. Many of these disparate languages have long-standing written literatures and alphabets. An impressive number of indigenous scripts and alphabets are to be found in West Africa alone, including the Mande syllabaries. The Mande syllabaries, or systems of writing, alone total up to five. These include the Vai, the Loma, and the Kpelle from Liberia, the Mende* from Sierra Leone, and the Bambara from northern Mali (Mande syllabaries are also found in Guinea and Ivory Coast). The overwhelming majority of African languages and cultures, those having written literatures and alphabets and those that do not, have long-standing traditions of oral literature by means of storytelling—a time-honored practice through which generations of young children continue to receive a crucial part of their substantive education.

*Note the distinction between Mande and Mende: Mande is a system of writings or group of languages common to Liberia and Sierra Leone, and Mende is the largest ethnolinguistic group in Sierra Leone.

Some Notable Geographical Features of Africa

Major Rivers

	miles
Nile	4,100
Congo	2,900
Niger	2,505
Zambezi	1,650
Shabeelle	1,550
Orange	1,155

Highest Mountains

	feet
Kilimanjaro, Tanzania	19,340
Kirinyaga, Kenya	17,058
Stanley, Congo	16,763
Ras Dashen, Ethiopia	15,158
Meru, Tanzania	14,979
Karisimbi, Rwanda-Congo	14,786
Elgon, Kenya-Uganda	14,178
Toubkal, Morocco	13,664
Cameroun, Cameroon	13,435
Thabana-Ntlenyana, Lesotho	11,425
Emi Koussi, Chad	11,204

Major Island Waters

	sq.miles
Lake Tanganyika	138,860
Lake Victoria	26,560
Lake Nyasa (Malawi)	8,680
Lake Chad	4,000–10,000*
Lake Albert	2,475
Lake Mweru	1,900
Lake Turkana (Kenya)	1,640

Island Nations**

	sq.miles
Madagascar	226,598
Cape Verde	1,557
Mauritius	787
Comoros	719
São Tomé & Príncipe	386
Seychelles	179

*The size of Lake Chad varies with the seasons, from 4,000 to 10,000 square miles.
**Other major islands include Reunion in the Indian Ocean; St. Helena and Ascension in the South Atlantic; Bioko in the Gulf of Guinea; and Madeira Island groups in the North Atlantic; and Bissagos Islands in the Atlantic (see map).

Data Sources: The *Columbia Encyclopedia* and the *Times Atlas of the World.* Other statistical data and research provided by Kimani C. Toussaint Jr., Ph.D., *Research Fellow at The James Franck Institute, University of Chicago, Department of Chemistry.*

THE FIVE MAJOR REGIONS OF AFRICA AND THEIR CHIEF EXPORTS

North Africa or Northern Africa

Countries or Territories	Chief Exports
Algeria — Sudan Egypt — Tunisia Libya — Morocco Western Sahara	oil & natural gas, phosphates, petroleum, agricultural products, cotton & textiles

East Africa or Eastern Africa

Countries or Territories	Chief Exports
Kenya • Eritrea • Tanzania Burundi • Uganda • Rwanda Djibouti • Ethiopia • Somalia	coffee, tea, cotton, pyrethrum

West Africa

Countries or Territories	Chief Exports
Benin • Guinea • Nigeria • Ghana Burkina Faso • Guinea-Bissau Senegal • Cape Verde • Liberia Sierra Leone • Côte d'Ivoire • Mali Togo Gambia • Mauritania • Niger	coal, limestone, oil, cotton, cocoa, palm oil, peanuts, timber, gold, tin, columbite, petroleum, diamonds, manganese, bauxite, copper, rubber, coffee, phosphate, coffee, zinc, natural gas & titanium

Central Africa

Countries or Territories	Chief Exports
Central African Republic Zaire • Congo • Gabon Cameroon • Cabinda Equatorial Guinea Sudan • Chad	petroleum, coffee, cocoa, cotton, tobacco, sugar, palm oil, manganese, uranium, gold, iron oil, titanium, sorghum

South Africa or Southern Africa

Countries or Territories	Chief Exports
Angola • Mozambique • Namibia • Swaziland Zambia • South Africa • Malawi • Lesotho Botswana • Madagascar • Zimbabwe	diamonds, nickel, copper, gold, platinum, agricultural products, uranium, petroleum, phosphate, natural gas, lead, tin, zinc, lithium, cadmium, manganese, chromium, sugar, cotton, tobacco, Iron, vanadium, sugarcane

K. Christopher Toussaint was born and raised in Orangeburg, South Carolina. He lived in Nigeria for more than twelve years with his Nigerian wife, Alice. There he gained a wealth of valuable knowledge about African educational systems and the exceedingly important role fables and storytelling can play in the whole process of educating young children. Although living mostly in an urban center (Benin City), he spent a great deal of his time in the rural villages talking and interacting with elderly villagers and listening to their old folktales and stories. Toussaint holds a B. B. A. from the Wharton School of Business, University of Pennsylvania, and an M. A. and Ph.D. in sociology from Temple University in Philadelphia. He has taught sociology at a number of leading colleges and universities, including the University of Pennsylvania. He is president and founder of the United African Educational Foundation (UAEF), a nonprofit, charitable organization whose primary aim is to provide educational support to needy African-origin schoolchildren in the United States and abroad. UAEF, the publisher of this book, is developing and issuing a series of these African fables and tales both as a primary means of fostering good social values among children and of financing the foundation's educational support programs and objectives.

Higgins Bond is an incredibly gifted artist with more than twenty-five years of experience illustrating everything from children's books to postage stamps. She is a native of Little Rock, Arkansas, holds a Bachelor of Fine Arts degree from the Memphis College of Art, and is a member of the prestigious Society of Illustrators. Bond has amassed an impressive array of honors and awards in the course of her professional career, including a medal of honor from the then Governor Bill Clinton and exhibitions at the Metropolitan Museum of Art and the DuSable Museum of African-American Art in Chicago. Bond has illustrated more than thirty books for children and adults and is the illustrator of three stamps for the United States Postal Service and four stamps for the United Nations Postal Administration. Other notable clients are: The Smithsonian Institution, Essence and Black Enterprise magazines, The Bradford Exchange, McGraw Hill Publishing Company, The Franklin Mint, NBC Television, Hennessy, Cognac, Anheuser-Busch, Frito-Lay, Columbia House, and others. Many of Bond's original images have been published by some of the country's largest collector-plate companies. Possessing such exceptionally rare talent, Bond can be best defined as an artist's artist or an illustrator's illustrator.